Captured Memories

Workbook

LOOKING BACK EDITION

Captured Memories Workbook: Looking Back Edition
Published by Memories in Writing

A previous edition of this book was published in 2004 by BWD Publishing LLC.
It is reprinted in arrangements with the author and original publisher.

Printed and bound in the United States of America

Visit our website at www.MemoriesInWriting.com
www.CapturedMemoriesWorkbook.com

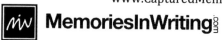 **MemoriesInWriting**

Captured Memories Workbook: Looking Back Edition republished 2012

ISBN: 978-0-9885470-2-5

Captured Memories
Workbook

Memories are priceless. They're the special moments that shape your life story. They're your treasures, but they're also your family's treasures. The Captured Memories Workbooks guide you through life's memorable moments, milestones, and passages. They're an easy-to-use and enjoyable way to start a memoir, or to preserve your life story for yourself, your children, or your grandchildren.

Our Captured Memories Workbook: Looking Back Edition gives you the guidance and inspiration to create your do-it-yourself memoir. With over 200 thought-provoking questions carefully chosen to guide you through life's twists and turns, our Workbook covers such stages as Early Years, Adulthood, Dating, Marriage, Parenting, Beliefs, Opinions, and more. With sections that focus on life stages as well as the events and forces that shaped your worldview, you'll have plenty of inspiration and guidance to dig deep. Extra pages in each section allow you to include additional comments, insights, or memories—making yours one-of-a-kind.

Once done, the completed workbook makes a precious keepsake for friends, family, or future generations. And, 5% of the proceeds from each Captured Memories Workbook goes to Alzheimer's Research, Care & Support.

Custom Publishing
We're proud to offer a custom publishing option for finished Captured Memories Workbooks. Once you've completed your Workbook, you can mail it, along with a selection of photos, documents, and other special memorabilia, to Memories In Writing. We'll transform it into a comprehensive narrative starring the writer. Finished books are hardbound, full-color 8.5 x 11" keepsakes, offering a polished story that ordinary photo albums and scrapbooks can't. Information and pricing is provided on page 197

CONTENTS

TIPS FOR COMPLETING YOUR WORKBOOK:

- Summarizing memories in a few paragraphs is not easy. When answering the questions think about who it is that you are sharing your memories with and exactly what you would like to communicate.

- Be specific and descriptive when answering the questions. (*Provide full names, dates, locations/addresses, etc.*)

- Leave blank the questions that do not apply.

MY MEMORIES:

_____

Name

_____

Date Began

_____

Date Completed

INTRODUCTION

Who are the main characters in your life story?
In this section, the writer introduces him or herself
and the members of his or her family.

What is your name?

_____

What is the name that you were given at birth?

_____

If there is a reason you were given this name?
I was given this name because...

_____

_____

_____

What is your date of birth and where were you born?

Date of birth:

Year: _____ Day: _____ Month: _____

Location of birth:

Country: _____

City: _____ State: _____

What was your hair and eye color when you were young?

Hair: _____ Color: _____

Were you born with any distinctive features?
(Example: I was born with one dimple and a star shaped birthmark on my wrist)

_____

_____

What are your parents' names, birth dates and locations of birth?

Mother's name:

Birth Name: _____

Married Name (s):

_____Year: _____

_____Year: _____

_____Year: _____

Date of birth:

Year: _____ Day: _____ Month: _____

Location of birth:

Country: _____

City: _____ State: _____

Father's name:

Birth Name:

_____

_____

Date of birth:

Year: _____ Day: _____ Month: _____

Location of birth:

Country: _____

City: _____ State: _____

What are your grandparents' names, birth dates and locations of birth?

Maternal Grandmother's name:

Birth Name:

_____

Married Name (s):

_____ Year: _____

_____ Year: _____

_____ Year: _____

Date of birth:

Year: _____ Day: _____ Month: _____

Location of birth:

Country: _____

City: _____ State: _____

Maternal Grandfather's name:

Birth Name:

_____

_____

Date of birth:

Year: _____ Day: _____ Month: _____

Location of birth:

Country: _____

City: _____ State: _____

What are your grandparents' names, birth dates and locations of birth?

Paternal Grandmother's name:

Birth Name:

_____

Married Name (s):

_____ Year: _____

_____ Year: _____

_____ Year: _____

Date of birth:

Year: _____ Day: _____ Month: _____

Location of birth:

Country: _____

City: _____ State: _____

Paternal Grandfather's name:

Birth Name:

_____

_____

Date of birth:

Year: _____ Day: _____ Month: _____

Location of birth:

Country: _____

City: _____ State: _____

What do you remember most about your grandparents?

Do you remember your great-grandparents? What do you remember most about them?

(Include their name(s) and what you remember most)

Who is the oldest family member that you remember? What do you remember most about them?

(Include their name(s) and what you remember most)

My siblings are: (Name, Birthdate, Birth Location)

□Brother □Sister

Name: _____

Date of Birth - Year: _____ Day: _____ Month: _____

Location of birth: Country: _____

City: _____ State: _____

□Brother □Sister

Name: _____

Date of Birth - Year: _____ Day: _____ Month: _____

Location of birth: Country: _____

City: _____ State: _____

□Brother □Sister

Name: _____

Date of Birth - Year: _____ Day: _____ Month: _____

Location of birth: Country: _____

City: _____ State: _____

□Brother □Sister

Name: _____

Date of Birth - Year: _____ Day: _____ Month: _____

Location of birth: Country: _____

City: _____ State: _____

My siblings are: (Name, Birthdate, Birth Location)

□Brother   □Sister

Name: _____

Date of Birth - Year: _____ Day: _____ Month: _____

Location of birth: Country: _____

City: _____ State: _____

□Brother   □Sister

Name: _____

Date of Birth - Year: _____ Day: _____ Month: _____

Location of birth: Country: _____

City: _____ State: _____

□Brother   □Sister

Name: _____

Date of Birth - Year: _____ Day: _____ Month: _____

Location of birth: Country: _____

City: _____ State: _____

□Brother   □Sister

Name: _____

Date of Birth - Year: _____ Day: _____ Month: _____

Location of birth: Country: _____

City: _____ State: _____

My siblings are: (Name, Birthdate, Birth Location)

□Brother □Sister

Name: _____

Date of Birth - Year: _____ Day:_____ Month: _____

Location of birth: Country: _____

City: _____ State: _____

□Brother □Sister

Name: _____

Date of Birth - Year: _____ Day:_____ Month: _____

Location of birth: Country: _____

City: _____ State: _____

□Brother □Sister

Name: _____

Date of Birth - Year: _____ Day:_____ Month: _____

Location of birth: Country: _____

City: _____ State: _____

□Brother □Sister

Name: _____

Date of Birth - Year: _____ Day:_____ Month: _____

Location of birth: Country: _____

City: _____ State: _____

My siblings are: (Name, Birthdate, Birth Location)

☐Brother ☐Sister

Name: _____

Date of Birth - Year: _____ Day: _____ Month: _____

Location of birth: Country: _____

City: _____ State: _____

☐Brother ☐Sister

Name: _____

Date of Birth - Year: _____ Day: _____ Month: _____

Location of birth: Country: _____

City: _____ State: _____

☐Brother ☐Sister

Name: _____

Date of Birth - Year: _____ Day: _____ Month: _____

Location of birth: Country: _____

City: _____ State: _____

☐Brother ☐Sister

Name: _____

Date of Birth - Year: _____ Day: _____ Month: _____

Location of birth: Country: _____

City: _____ State: _____

Use this page to include additional comments, insights, or memories that you would like to add to this chapter.

Use this page to include additional comments, insights, or memories that you would like to add to this chapter.

Use this page to include additional comments, insights, or memories that you would like to add to this chapter.

GROWING UP

What was your childhood like?

Childhood is, for some, a magical time. The Growing-Up section helps the writer recall and share what the world was like and what they learned during childhood.

MemoriesInWriting
400 S Main St., Unit 1392 - Travelers Rest, SC 29690
1-800-604-9843

Packing Slip

Order Information
Order Number: 152529

Date: 11/8/2016 5:01 PM

Shipping Method: USPS

Ship To
Dorothy Winina
11903 Singleton Drive
La Mirada, CA 90638
United States
Phone:1234567890

Product Information

Product Name	Part No.	Quantity
Captured Memories Workbook: Looking Back Edition	9780988547025	1

Where did your parents work?

Mother:

_____

_____

_____

_____

Father:

_____

_____

_____

_____

Describe the house and neighborhood where you grew up.
Example: I lived in a small red brick house on a farm and most days I would go outside and...

_____

_____

_____

_____

_____

_____

_____

_____

_____

_____

_____

What was a typical day like in your home?

Example: Most mornings my mom would ___ while my dad and I ___

Share something that you enjoyed doing as a child.

Example: On the weekend I really enjoyed playing __ with __ that lived down the road; I won most of the time.

Describe the relationship that you had with your siblings when you were young.

_____

_____

_____

_____

_____

_____

_____

_____

_____

_____

_____

_____

_____

_____

_____

_____

_____

_____

_____

_____

_____

_____

_____

_____

Did you have a special/close relationship with any of your siblings? *Provide their name and why you were close.*

_____

_____

_____

_____

_____

_____

_____

_____

_____

_____

Were any of your siblings annoying?
Provide their name and why you considered them to be annoying.

_____

_____

_____

_____

_____

_____

_____

_____

_____

_____

_____

Are there any stories that you would like to share about your siblings?

Example: I was the ____ of ____ children, my brother ____ would often defend me after I was caught ____

Describe the relationship that you had with your mother and/or father when you were young?

Are there any stories that you would like to share about your mother and/or father?

Did you have any family traditions or memorable holiday activities when your were younger? If yes, describe in detail below

Vacations make lifelong memories (good or bad). Describe any memorable vacations you took or travel you did when you were younger. Where did you go? Why is this vacation memorable?

Share a pleasant memory from your childhood. Why does this memory stand out for you? Include as many details as you can.

Now, recall an unpleasant memory from your childhood. Why does this unpleasant memory stick with you? Sometimes, these memories are events in your life that you have not yet shared with your children or other family members.

The names of the elementary / grade school(s) that you attended:

School Name: _____

Year(s):_____ Grades Attended: _____

Country: _____

City: _____ State: _____

School Name: _____

Year(s): _____ Grades Attended: _____

Country: _____

City: _____ State: _____

School Name: _____

Year(s):_____ Grades Attended: _____

Country: _____

City:_____ State: _____

How did you get to school?

_____

_____

_____

_____

_____

_____

_____

What was the name your favorite elementary school teacher (if you had more than one favorite, include all names)? What did you learn from him or her? What subject(s) did you like best?

_____

_____

_____

_____

_____

_____

_____

Did you play sports or participate in any other school or extracurricular activites? If yes, what was the sport or activity? What did you enjoy most about it?

_____

_____

_____

_____

_____

_____

_____

_____

_____

Who are the friends you remember from your elementary/grade school years, and what about them stands out in your memory? What were their names? What games did you play with them?

Use this page to include additional comments, insights, or memories about your elementary / grade school years.

What was the name of the high school(s) you attended:

School Name: _____

Year(s): _____ Grades Attended: _____

Country: _____

City: _____ State: _____

School Name: _____

Year(s): _____ Grades Attended: _____

Country: _____

City: _____ State: _____

School Name: _____

Year(s): _____ Grades Attended: _____

Country: _____

City: _____ State: _____

How did you get to school?

_____

_____

_____

_____

_____

_____

_____

_____

What was the name your favorite high school teacher (if you had more than one favorite, include all names)? What did you learn from him or her? What subject(s) did you like best?

_____

_____

_____

_____

_____

_____

_____

_____

Did you play sports or participate in any other school or extracurricular activites? If yes, what was the sport or activity? What did you enjoy most about it?

_____

_____

_____

_____

_____

_____

_____

_____

Who are the friends you remember from your elementary/grade school years, and what about them stands out in your memory? What were their names? What games did you play with them?

Use this page to include additional comments, insights, or memories about your high school years.

_____

_____

_____

_____

_____

_____

_____

_____

_____

_____

_____

_____

_____

_____

_____

_____

_____

_____

_____

_____

_____

Describe a fad that you participated in or observed when you were growing up?

_____

_____

_____

_____

_____

_____

How old were you when you started dating?

_____

_____

_____

Describe your first date?

_____

_____

_____

_____

_____

_____

_____

_____

Did you and your friends have a special place where you liked to go and have fun? *Describe where it was and what did you and your friends do.*

_____

_____

_____

_____

_____

_____

_____

_____

_____

_____

_____

_____

_____

_____

_____

_____

_____

_____

_____

_____

_____

_____

How old were you when you received your driving license?

_____

_____

Everyone has a first car, and everyone has a story about it. Describe the first automobile you drove. What was the make, model, and year? What color was it? What do you remember most about that vehicle?

_____

_____

_____

_____

_____

_____

_____

_____

_____

_____

_____

_____

_____

_____

_____

_____

_____

_____

What was your first job? Was it a paper route, working at the local candy store, or collecting eggs on the farm—or maybe something else? How did you get the job? Who did you work for? Do you recall how much you were paid? If so, include that information as well.

If you attended college, where did you go? Where was the college located? Please provide details on the college(s) you attended as well as what influenced your choice (location? tradition? family?).

_____

_____

_____

_____

_____

_____

_____

_____

School Name: _____

Country: _____

City: _____ State: _____

Year(s): _____ Major: _____

Degree(s): _____

_____

School Name: _____

Country: _____

City: _____ State: _____

Year(s): _____ Major: _____

Degree(s): _____

_____

Did you have a job while attending college? If so, what did you do, where did you work, and what were you paid? (for example, "I made $100 per week"). College jobs are sometimes the springboard to careers, so provide as many details as possible.

What are the life lessons that you learned during this period in your life? What can you share about them, and how have those lessons influenced your life since?

Are there any life lessons that you learned during this period in your life that you would like to share?

Use this page to include additional comments, insights, or memories that you would like to add to this chapter.

Use this page to include additional comments, insights, or memories that you would like to add to this chapter.

ADULTHOOD

When you look back, can you see how far you came?
Embarking on life as an adult can be both exciting and
terrifying. Here, writers describe careers, a stint in the
military service, and their adult family lives.

Describe your first apartment or house. Where was it located? How did you find it? Did you have a roommate—and if so, what was his or her name? What did the home look like and what do you remember most about it?

_____

_____

_____

_____

_____

_____

_____

_____

_____

_____

_____

_____

_____

_____

_____

_____

_____

_____

_____

_____

_____

_____

Country: _____

City: _____ State: _____

Year(s):_____

Describe the neighborhood

Describe your first piece of furniture, where did you get it?

Describe any memorable vacations you took or travel (good or bad) you did before getting married or having children. Where did you go? Why did you decide to go there?

Share a pleasant memory from your early adulthood. Why does this memory stand out for you? Include as many details as you can.

Now, recall an unpleasant memory from your early adulthood. Why does this unpleasant memory stick with you? Sometimes, these memories are events in your life that you have not yet shared with your children or other family members.

EMPLOYMENT

What was your first job as an adult?

_____

_____

_____

_____

How did you decide on your career?

_____

_____

_____

_____

_____

_____

What were the name(s) of the companies where you were employed, job title and the year(s) of employment?

Company Name: _____

Country: _____

City: _____ State: _____

Year(s): _____ - _____

Brief description of job duties: _____

_____

_____

_____

Company Name: _____

Country: _____

City: _____ State: _____

Year(s):_____ - _____

Brief description of job duties: _____

_____

_____

_____

Company Name: _____

Country: _____

City: _____ State: _____

Year(s):_____ - _____

Brief description of job duties: _____

_____

_____

_____

Company Name: _____

Country: _____

City: _____ State: _____

Year(s):_____ - _____

Brief description of job duties: _____

_____

_____

_____

Is there a colleague, boss, or employee whom you remember most from your work years? If yes, who is it, and why is he or she memorable to you?

What are/were the most significant changes that you have observed in the workplace?

What are the life lessons that you learned during this period in your life? What can you share about them, and how have those lessons influenced your life since?

What year did you retire and how old were you?

Year: _____   Age: _____

What do you remember most about the months / weeks leading up to your retirement?

_____

_____

_____

_____

_____

_____

_____

_____

_____

_____

_____

_____

_____

_____

_____

_____

_____

_____

_____

Did you do anything memorable immediately after you retired? If so, describe what you did and why it is memorable.

Have you done everything that you planned to do during retirement? If not, what do you still desire to do? What was your number one goal for your retirement? Have you accomplished it?

MILITARY SERVICE

If you served in the military, when and where did you serve, which branch of the military, rank and duties?

Military Unit: _____

Years of service: _____ - _____

Military Base: _____

Country: _____

City: _____ State: _____

Year(s): _____ - _____

Description (share memories from this time):

_____

_____

_____

_____

_____

_____

_____

_____

_____

_____

_____

Military Base: _____

Country: _____

City: _____ State: _____

Year(s): _____ - _____

Description (share memories from this time):

_____

_____

_____

_____

_____

_____

_____

Military Base: _____

Country: _____

City: _____ State: _____

Year(s): _____ - _____

Description (share memories from this time):

_____

_____

_____

_____

_____

_____

_____

If you were injured in the line of duty, what were the circumstances and what were your injuires?

_____

_____

_____

_____

_____

_____

If you served in a war, which war? When and where was it? What were your duties and how did you feel about this war?

_____

_____

_____

_____

_____

_____

_____

_____

_____

_____

_____

_____

_____

Are there any events/memories other than the ones that you have already shared that stand out during your military years? Include as many details as you can.

MARRIAGE

What is your spouse's name and date of birth?

Name: _____

Date of Birth: - Year: _____ Day: _____ Month: _____

Location of birth: Country: _____

City: _____ State: _____

Describe how you met your spouse. Provide details (how did you meet, location, date, etc.)

_____

_____

_____

_____

_____

_____

_____

_____

_____

_____

_____

_____

_____

_____

_____

_____

When you first met your future spouse, what was your first impression of him or her?

Describe your first date?

What do you remember most about dating before you got married?

How long did you date before you got engaged?

_____

_____

When did you get engaged?

Year: _____ Day: _____ Month: _____

Describe the marriage proposal

_____

_____

_____

_____

_____

_____

_____

_____

_____

_____

_____

_____

_____

_____

_____

_____

When did you get married (wedding date)?

Year: _____ Day: _____ Month: _____

Where were you married?

Location: Country: _____

City: _____ State: _____

Describe your wedding ceremony?

_____
_____
_____
_____
_____
_____
_____
_____
_____
_____
_____
_____
_____
_____
_____
_____
_____

Think back to your wedding day. What do you remember most about your bride or groom on that day? Was he cool as a cucumber? What she nervous?

WEDDING PARTY
Introduce the wedding party

Name: _____

Role in wedding: _____

Relationship: _____

Comment: _____

_____

Name: _____

Role in wedding: _____

Relationship: _____

Comment: _____

_____

Name: _____

Role in wedding: _____

Relationship: _____

Comment: _____

_____

Name: _____

Role in wedding: _____

Relationship: _____

Comment: _____

_____

WEDDING PARTY
Introduce the wedding party

Name: _____

Role in wedding: _____

Relationship: _____

Comment: _____

_____

Name: _____

Role in wedding: _____

Relationship: _____

Comment: _____

_____

Name: _____

Role in wedding: _____

Relationship: _____

Comment: _____

_____

Name: _____

Role in wedding: _____

Relationship: _____

Comment: _____

_____

What do you remember most about your wedding day?

Did you go on a honeymoon? If yes, where did you go?

Country: _____

City: _____ State: _____

_____

What do you remember most about your honeymoon?

_____
_____
_____
_____
_____
_____
_____
_____
_____
_____
_____
_____
_____
_____
_____
_____
_____

Describe the first house or apartment where you and your spouse lived and what you remember most about living there.

Country: _____

City: _____ State: _____

_____

_____

_____

_____

_____

_____

_____

_____

_____

_____

_____

_____

_____

_____

_____

_____

_____

_____

_____

_____

_____

_____

_____

Describe your first significant purchase as a newlywed couple (i.e. furniture, car, pool)?

What do you remember most about life as newlyweds? What surprised you the most?

As your relationship grew and matured, what was its most significant change from your time as newlyweds?

How would you describe your spouse?
What do/did you admire most about him/her?

Is there anything about your spouse that you would like to share that may not have been covered in earlier questions? Sometimes, these memories are something that you have not yet shared with your children or other family members.

Describe any memorable vacations you and your spouse took or travel you did before having children. Where did you go? Why did you decide to go there?

How many years have you been married (or were you married)?

_____ □Day(s)   □Month(s)   □Year(s)

What are your personal life lessons about marriage? From the vantage point of time and experience, what would you like to share?

_____

_____

_____

_____

_____

_____

_____

_____

_____

_____

_____

_____

_____

_____

_____

_____

_____

_____

_____

Use this page to include additional comments, insights, or memories that you would like to add about selecting a spouse and marriage.

<u>Second Marriage</u>

What is your spouse's name and date of birth?

Name: _____

Date of Birth - Year: _____ Day: _____ Month: _____

Location of birth: Country: _____

City: _____ State: _____

How and when did you meet your spouse (month & year)

_____

_____

_____

_____

_____

_____

When you first met your future spouse, what was your first impression of him or her?

_____

_____

_____

_____

_____

_____

How long did you date before you got engaged?

_____

_____

When did you get engaged?

Year: _____ Day: _____ Month: _____

Describe your marriage proposal

_____

_____

_____

_____

_____

_____

_____

_____

_____

_____

_____

_____

_____

_____

_____

_____

_____

_____

When did you get married (wedding date)?

Year: _____ Day: _____ Month: _____

Describe your wedding ceremony?

_____

_____

_____

_____

_____

_____

_____

_____

_____

_____

_____

_____

_____

Did you go on a honeymoon? If so, where did you go?

Country: _____

City: _____ State: _____

_____

_____

How would you describe your spouse?
What do/did you admire most about him/her?

_____

_____

_____

_____

_____

_____

_____

Are there any events/memories that stand out, tell us about them?

_____

_____

_____

_____

_____

_____

_____

_____

How many years have you been married (or were you married)?

_____ □Day(s)   □Month(s)   □Year(s)

What are your personal life lessons about marriage? From the vantage point of time and experience, what would you like to share?

_____

_____

_____

_____

_____

_____

_____

_____

_____

_____

_____

_____

_____

_____

_____

_____

_____

_____

Third Marriage

What is your spouse's name and date of birth?

Name: _____

Date of Birth: - Year: _____ Day: _____ Month: _____

Location of birth: Country: _____

City: _____ State: _____

How did you meet your spouse ?

_____

_____

_____

_____

How long did you date before you got engaged?

_____

_____

When did you get engaged?

Year: _____ Day: _____ Month: _____

_____

When and where did you get married (wedding date)?

Year: _____ Day: _____ Month: _____

Country: _____

City: _____ State: _____

Did you go on a honeymoon? If so, where did you go?

Country: _____

City: _____ State: _____

_____

_____

How would you describe your spouse?
What do/did you admire most about him/her?

_____

_____

_____

_____

_____

_____

_____

Are there any events/memories that stand out, tell us about them?

_____

_____

_____

_____

_____

_____

_____

How many years have you been married (or were you married)?

_____ Select one: □Day(s) □Month(s) □Year(s)

What are your personal life lessons about marriage? From the vantage point of time and experience, what would you like to share?

_____

_____

_____

_____

_____

_____

_____

_____

_____

_____

_____

_____

_____

_____

_____

_____

PARENTING

My children are: (Name, Birthdate, Birth Location)

□Son □Daughter

Name: _____

Birth Date: Year: _____ Day: _____ Month: _____

Location of birth: Country: _____

City: _____ State: _____

□Son □Daughter

Name: _____

Birth Date: Year: _____ Day: _____ Month: _____

Location of birth: Country: _____

City: _____ State: _____

□Son □Daughter

Name: _____

Birth Date: Year: _____ Day: _____ Month: _____

Location of birth: Country: _____

City: _____ State: _____

□Son □Daughter

Name: _____

Birth Date: Year: _____ Day: _____ Month: _____

Location of birth: Country: _____

City: _____ State: _____

My children are: (Name, Birthdate, Birth Location)

☐Son ☐Daughter

Name: _____

Birth Date: Year: _____ Day: _____ Month: _____

Location of birth: Country: _____

City: _____ State: _____

☐Son ☐Daughter

Name: _____

Birth Date: Year: _____ Day: _____ Month: _____

Location of birth: Country: _____

City: _____ State: _____

☐Son ☐Daughter

Name: _____

Birth Date: Year: _____ Day: _____ Month: _____

Location of birth: Country: _____

City: _____ State: _____

☐Son ☐Daughter

Name: _____

Birth Date: Year: _____ Day: _____ Month: _____

Location of birth: Country: _____

City: _____ State: _____

My children are: (Name, Birthdate, Birth Location)

□Son □Daughter

Name: _____

Birth Date: Year: _____ Day: _____ Month: _____

Location of birth: Country: _____

City: _____ State: _____

□Son □Daughter

Name: _____

Birth Date: Year: _____ Day: _____ Month: _____

Location of birth: Country: _____

City: _____ State: _____

□Son □Daughter

Name: _____

Birth Date: Year: _____ Day: _____ Month: _____

Location of birth: Country: _____

City: _____ State: _____

□Son □Daughter

Name: _____

Birth Date: Year: _____ Day: _____ Month: _____

Location of birth: Country: _____

City: _____ State: _____

How did you find out that you were going to be a parent for the first time? How did you feel about it?

Do you have any memories about the birth of your child/children that stand out, if so, provide the name of the child and share what you remember most.

What is the funniest thing that you can remember your child/children saying or doing? Include as many details as you can.

Please share a favorite memory about your child/children. Include as many details as you can.

What have you found most rewarding about being a parent?

What did you find most difficult about being a parent?

Are there any life lessons about parenting that you would like to share?

If you were able to do it all over again, would you change the way you raised your child/children? If yes, What would you do differently?

How did you find out that you were going to be a grandparent for the first time? How did you feel about it?

Share any stories that stand out about your grandchildren. Include as many details as you can.

Use this page to include additional comments, insights, or memories that you would like to add to this chapter.

_____

_____

_____

_____

_____

_____

_____

_____

_____

_____

_____

_____

_____

_____

_____

_____

_____

_____

_____

_____

_____

_____

Use this page to include additional comments, insights, or memories that you would like to add to this chapter.

_____

_____

_____

_____

_____

_____

_____

_____

_____

_____

_____

_____

_____

_____

_____

_____

_____

_____

_____

_____

_____

HISTORICAL EVENTS

What events shaped the world for you?
Having lived through much of the twentieth century,
seniors have been witness to many changes in society,
technology, politics, and the arts. Here, writers share
memories of the major historical events in their lives.
They also share thoughts that shaped their worldview.

What wars have been fought during your lifetime? How did you feel about them?

When was the first presidential election in which you voted? Who were the candidates? What do you remember of the issues and the country's mood?

What U.S. President(s) have you admired the most and why?

_____

_____

_____

_____

_____

_____

_____

What do you remember about the day President Kennedy was assasinated?

_____

_____

_____

_____

_____

_____

_____

_____

_____

_____

Do you remember the Great Depression? If yes, describe what do you remember most?

_____

_____

_____

_____

_____

_____

_____

_____

_____

_____

If you remember segregation? Describe the impact it had on your life/community.

_____

_____

_____

_____

_____

_____

_____

_____

_____

If you remember the Holocaust? Describe the impact it had on your life/community.

_____

_____

_____

_____

_____

_____

_____

_____

_____

_____

What do you remember most about women's rights?

_____

_____

_____

_____

_____

_____

_____

_____

_____

_____

What changes in technology during your lifetime do you feel have had the greatest impact on civilization? Why?

What do you remember most about the 1950's

What do you remember most about the 1960's

What do you remember most about the 1970's

What do you remember most about the 1980's

What do you remember most about the 1990's?

What do you remember most about the 2000's?

What other major historical events have occurred during your lifetime? How have these events, in your opinion, shaped the country? How did they affect your life or community? And, how have they influenced your worldview?

What other major historical events have occurred during your lifetime? How have these events, in your opinion, shaped the country? How did they affect your life or community? And, how have they influenced your worldview?

Use this page to include additional comments, insights, or memories that you would like to add to this chapter.

Use this page to include additional comments, insights, or memories that you would like to add to this chapter.

MY PETS

Who were your four-footed friends?
Here, writers can tell the stories and memories of the
pets who shared their lives

Use this section to tell the stories and memories of the pets who shared your life   Include as many details as you can. Include pet name, type of animal, how old you were and the impact they had on your life.

Use this section to tell the stories and memories of the pets who shared your life   Include as many details as you can. Include pet name, type of animal, how old you were and the impact they had on your life.

Use this section to tell the stories and memories of the pets who shared your life   Include as many details as you can. Include pet name, type of animal, how old you were and the impact they had on your life.

Use this section to tell the stories and memories of the pets who shared your life   Include as many details as you can. Include pet name, type of animal, how old you were and the impact they had on your life.

PEOPLE IN MY LIFE

Who else shaped you and changed the course your life?
This section is for participants to acknowledge the people
who have touched and inspired them: friends, bosses,
students, teachers, and mentors, for instance.
It's also a section to capture the other players in the
writer's life story.

Use this section to acknowledge the people who have touched and inspired you that were not captured in earlier chapters: friends, bosses, students, teachers, and mentors, for instance. Include as many details as you can. What was their name and why did they had a memorable impact on your life?

Use this section to acknowledge the people who have touched and inspired you that were not captured in earlier chapters: friends, bosses, students, teachers, and mentors, for instance. Include as many details as you can. What was their name and why did they had a memorable impact on your life?

Use this section to acknowledge the people who have touched and inspired you that were not captured in earlier chapters: friends, bosses, students, teachers, and mentors, for instance. Include as many details as you can. What was their name and why did they had a memorable impact on your life?

Use this section to acknowledge the people who have touched and inspired you that were not captured in earlier chapters: friends, bosses, students, teachers, and mentors, for instance. Include as many details as you can. What was their name and why did they had a memorable impact on your life?

HOBBIES / ENTERTAINMENT

What brought you joy? Did you have a special talent?
Writers recall their talents and gifts, their hobbies, and their favorite entertainment—what they looked forward to most about the lighter side of life.

What are your favorite hobbies? How did you start this hobby. Include as many details as you can.

What are your favorite hobbies? How did you start this hobby. Include as many details as you can.

What part did music, literature, theater, concerts, radio, movies and television play in your life?

What part did music, literature, theater, concerts, radio, movies and television play in your life?

BELIEFS AND OPINIONS

What beliefs do you hold dear?
Participants give insight into their beliefs and opinions on
an array of topics, including religious or spiritual beliefs,
their predictions for major world events, and more.

Describe your religious/spiritual beliefs?

What would you like to share about your beliefs that you want your family to remember?

How would you describe yourself politically? Why?

From your perspective, what are the biggest problems currently facing our nation? And how, in your opinion, do you think they can be addressed or solved?

What do you feel will be the next major world event? When, Where and Why?

What human characteristics have you valued most—in yourself, or in others—and why do you think they're so positive? How have you cultivated them or sought them out in your life?

What are the human characteristics or tendencies you consider most destructive? What dark side have you struggled with yourself?

Do you have any special traditions? Include as many details as you can. Why did you begin this tradition?

Use this page to include additional comments, insights, or memories that you would like to add to this chapter.

_____

_____

_____

_____

_____

_____

_____

_____

_____

_____

_____

_____

_____

_____

_____

_____

_____

_____

_____

_____

_____

_____

_____

_____

Use this page to include additional comments, insights, or memories that you would like to add to this chapter.

FYI

This section is for participants to provide information about them that defies any singular category.
The section asks such questions as
Why are you living where you are today?
What are your bad habits?
If you could change something about yourself,
what would you change?

From this vantage point, what are the hardest personal choices that you have made? What made them difficult? Do you feel now that you made the right choices? Why?

Why are you living where you live today?

_____

_____

_____

_____

_____

_____

_____

_____

Do you wish you lived some place else? If yes, where would you live?

_____

_____

_____

_____

_____

_____

_____

_____

Describe your general health

_____

_____

_____

_____

_____

_____

_____

_____

_____

_____

_____

Have you had an major illnesses or health problems ?

_____

_____

_____

_____

_____

_____

_____

_____

_____

_____

Do you have any health problems that are considered hereditary? If yes, Include as many details as you can.

_____

_____

_____

_____

_____

_____

_____

_____

_____

_____

Have you ever been hospitalized extended time due to a medical illness? If yes, Include as many details as you can.

_____

_____

_____

_____

_____

_____

_____

_____

_____

_____

Do you have any habits (good or bad) now or in the past? What are/were they? Include as many details as you can.

Have you ever been the victim of a violent crime? If yes, Include as many details as you can.

_____

_____

_____

_____

_____

_____

_____

_____

_____

_____

If you could change something about yourself, what would you change?

_____

_____

_____

_____

_____

_____

_____

_____

_____

What is the most exciting thing that has ever happened to you? Was it a personal triumph or accomplishment? Did you meet someone famous? Capture everything you can about the experience, whatever it was.

What accomplishment of your own makes you most proud? Why?

When you looked into the mirror at the age of 30, what did you see (provide a description regarding your appearance)?

_____

_____

_____

_____

_____

_____

_____

_____

_____

_____

When you look into the mirror at your current age: _____, what do you see (provide a description regarding your appearance)?

_____

_____

_____

_____

_____

_____

_____

_____

_____

_____

_____

What have you not done but have always wanted to do?

Use this page to include additional comments, insights, or memories that you would like to add to this chapter.

_____

_____

_____

_____

_____

_____

_____

_____

_____

_____

_____

_____

_____

_____

_____

_____

_____

_____

_____

_____

_____

_____

Use this page to include additional comments, insights, or memories that you would like to add to this chapter.

FAVORITES

What are a few of your favorite things?
Writers catalogue their favorites: song, holiday, book—
even recipes, so that others can prepare them in the future.

What is your favorite painting?

Who is your favorite musician or musical group?

What is your favorite poem?

What is your favorite TV program?

Who is your favorite author?

_____

_____

_____

_____

What is your favorite book?

_____

_____

_____

_____

What is your favorite season?

_____

_____

_____

_____

What is your favorite song?

_____

_____

_____

_____

What is your favorite flower?

_____

_____

_____

_____

What is your favorite holiday?

_____

_____

_____

_____

What is your favorite color?

_____

_____

_____

_____

What is your favorite sport?

_____

_____

_____

_____

Who is your favorite athlete?

_____

_____

_____

_____

What is your favorite candy?

_____

_____

_____

_____

What is your favorite cookie?

_____

_____

_____

_____

What is your favorite drink?

_____

_____

_____

_____

What is your favorite dessert?

_____

_____

_____

_____

Share the recipe if you have it.

_____

_____

_____

_____

_____

_____

_____

_____

_____

_____

_____

_____

_____

_____

_____

_____

What is your favorite entree?

_____

_____

_____

_____

_____

Share the recipe if you have it.

_____

_____

_____

_____

_____

_____

_____

_____

_____

_____

_____

_____

_____

_____

_____

_____

FAVORITE QUOTES:

What words do you live by?

This section prompts participants to jot down some of their favorite quotes.

Use this section to to jot down some of their favorite quotes.

Quote 1:

_____

_____

_____

_____

_____

_____

By:

_____

_____

Quote 2:

_____

_____

_____

_____

_____

_____

By:

_____

_____

Quote 3:

_____

_____

_____

_____

_____

_____

By:

_____

_____

Quote 4:

_____

_____

_____

_____

_____

_____

By:

_____

_____

NOTES

What else is precious to you?
Not everything fits neatly into a category. Here, writers
capture other memories, thoughts, and insights not
included elsewhere in their workbooks.

Use this page to include additional comments, insights, or memories that you would like to add to this chapter.

_____

_____

_____

_____

_____

_____

_____

_____

_____

_____

_____

_____

_____

_____

_____

_____

_____

_____

_____

_____

_____

_____

Use this page to include additional comments, insights, or memories that you would like to add to this chapter.

Use this page to include additional comments, insights, or memories that you would like to add to this chapter.

Use this page to include additional comments, insights, or memories that you would like to add to this chapter.

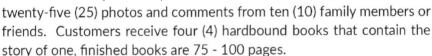

ORDER FORM

To order your custom books, complete Steps 1 – 4 and contact Memories In Writing at 800-604-9843 or online at www.MemoriesInWriting.com

☐ Step 1:

Use pages 202 - 208 to identify the photos or documents that you would like to include in your book. If you would like your finished books to contain comments from family or friends, have them complete "I will Never Forget When…" located on pages 209 - 215.

☐ Step 2: Complete the order form below

Description	Order Quantity	Cost Each	Total
Memories of One Package Includes 4 hardbound books (75 – 100 pages)		$550.00	
Extra books: Memories of One (hardbound)		$ 45.00	
Extra books: Memories of One (softbound) *Minimum order of 5 books required*		$ 30.00	
Memories of Two Package Includes 4 hardbound books (100 – 150 pages)		$850.00	
Extra books: Memories of Two (hardbound)		$ 55.00	
Extra books: Memories of Two (softbound) *Minimum order of 5 books required*		$ 35.00	
Additional Photos/Documents		$ 2.00	
Hard Copy Proof		$ 10.00	
Email Proof (we will email to the address provided in the ordered by section)		Free	
Captured Memories Workbook: Looking Back Edition Includes shipping & handling cost		$ 18.45	
		Subtotal	
		Expedite Charge	
		Order Credit *Coupon Discount and/or shipping credit amount provided when you place your order*	-
		Amount Enclosed	$

<u>Expedited Order Requests</u> (i.e. Family Reunion, Anniversary or birthday gift)
Call Memories In Writing at: 800-604-9843 for pricing and information

☐ Step 3:

Ordered By:

Daytime Phone (   ) _____

Email Address: _____

Name: _____

Address: _____

City: _____ State: _____ Zip code: _____

Ship To: ☐ Same as <u>Ordered By:</u> Information
Complete only if different than Ordered By Information:

Daytime Phone (   ) _____

Name: _____

Address: _____

City: _____ State: _____ Zip code: _____

Payment Information

☐ Check Enclosed: Make payments payable to: Memories in Writing LLC
☐ MasterCard   ☐ Visa   ☐ Discover   ☐ AmEx   ☐ Coupon Enclosed: _____

Account: _____

Exp. Date: _____ Security Code (3 or 4 digit code): _____

Name on Card: _____

Billing Information: ☐ Same as <u>Ordered By:</u> Information
Complete only if different than Ordered By Information:
Name: _____
Address: _____
City: _____ State: _____ Zip code: _____

☐ Step 4:

Place Your Order Now!
Call Memories In Writing at 1-800-604-9843
or visit us online at www.MemoriesInWriting.com

Enter Your Confirmation Number Here:
*This number was provided after you submitted
your order online or by a MIW Representative*

Memories In Writing LLC
400 S Main Street Unit 1392 – Travelers Rest, SC 29690

PHOTO/DOCUMENT
Identification Forms

Use this section to identify the photos and / or documents that you would like included in your finished book. All photos and documents provided are scanned and returned within 5 – 10 business days after order receipt.

Apply the corresponding photo description numbered label that was provided in your workbook submission packet to your photo or document.

Please include as many details as possible regarding your submission, this allows us to insert the material in the appropriate section of your book.

Photo / Documentation 01 Description:

_____

_____

_____

Photo / Documentation 02 Description:

_____

_____

_____

Photo / Documentation 03 Description:

_____

_____

_____

Photo / Documentation 04 Description:

_____

_____

_____

Photo / Documentation 05 Description:

_____

_____

_____

Photo / Documentation 06 Description:

_____

_____

_____

Photo / Documentation 07 Description:

_____

_____

_____

Photo / Documentation 08 Description:

_____

_____

_____

Photo / Documentation 09 Description:

_____

_____

_____

Photo / Documentation 10 Description:

_____

_____

_____

Photo / Documentation 11 Description:

_____

_____

_____

Photo / Documentation 12 Description:

_____

_____

_____

Photo / Documentation 13 Description:

_____

_____

_____

Photo / Documentation 14 Description:

_____

_____

_____

Photo / Documentation 15 Description:

_____

_____

_____

Photo / Documentation 16 Description:

_____

_____

_____

Photo / Documentation 17 Description:

_____

_____

_____

Photo / Documentation 18 Description:

_____

_____

_____

Photo / Documentation 19 Description:

_____

_____

_____

Photo / Documentation 20 Description:

_____

_____

_____

Photo / Documentation 21 Description:

_____

_____

_____

Photo / Documentation 22 Description:

_____

_____

_____

Photo / Documentation 23 Description:

_____

_____

_____

Photo / Documentation 24 Description:

_____

_____

_____

Photo / Documentation 25 Description:

_____

_____

_____

Photo / Documentation 26 Description:

_____

_____

_____

Photo / Documentation 27 Description:

_____

_____

_____

Photo / Documentation 28 Description:

_____

_____

_____

Photo / Documentation 29 Description:

_____

_____

_____

Photo / Documentation 30 Description:

_____

_____

_____

I WILL NEVER FORGET WHEN...

As an addition to your workbook or hardbound books, you can request that family members or friends add comments to this section.

Their comments will make a wonderful addition to your story.

I will never forget when...

_____

_____

_____

_____

_____

_____

_____

_____

Written By: _____

Date Written - Year: _____ Day: _____ Month: _____

I will never forget when...

_____

_____

_____

_____

_____

_____

_____

_____

Written By: _____

Date Written - Year: _____ Day: _____ Month: _____

I will never forget when...

_____

_____

_____

_____

_____

_____

_____

Written By: _____

Date Written - Year: _____ Day: _____ Month: _____

I will never forget when...

_____

_____

_____

_____

_____

_____

_____

Written By: _____

Date Written - Year: _____ Day: _____ Month: _____

I will never forget when...

_____

_____

_____

_____

_____

_____

_____

_____

Written By: _____

Date Written - Year: _____ Day: _____ Month: _____

I will never forget when...

_____

_____

_____

_____

_____

_____

_____

_____

Written By: _____

Date Written - Year: _____ Day: _____ Month: _____

I will never forget when...

_____
_____
_____
_____
_____
_____
_____

Written By: _____

Date Written - Year: _____ Day: _____ Month: _____

I will never forget when...

_____
_____
_____
_____
_____
_____
_____

Written By: _____

Date Written - Year: _____ Day: _____ Month: _____

I will never forget when...

_____

_____

_____

_____

_____

_____

_____

_____

Written By: _____

Date Written - Year: _____ Day: _____ Month: _____

I will never forget when...

_____

_____

_____

_____

_____

_____

_____

_____

Written By: _____

Date Written - Year: _____ Day: _____ Month: _____

Printed and bound in the United States of America

Visit our website at www.MemoriesInWriting.com

Captured Memories Workbook: Looking Back Edition republished 2012

ISBN: 978-0-9885470-2-5